STAR WARS

EXPERT GUIDE

This book
belongs to:

Penguin
Random
House

For Dorling Kindersley
Senior Editor Elizabeth Dowsett
Project Editor David Fentiman
Editors Shari Last, Julia March,
Helen Murray, Matt Jones
Project Art Editor Owen Bennett
Designer Toby Truphet
Additional design by Nathan Martin,
Lynne Moulding, David McDonald, Mark Penfound,
Rob Perry, Mark Richards, Clive Savage, Rhys Thomas
Senior Pre-Production Producer Rebecca Fallowfield
Producer Naomi Green
Managing Editor Sadie Smith
Managing Art Editor Ron Stobbart
Creative Manager Sarah Harland
Art Director Lisa Lanzarini
Publisher Julie Ferris
Publishing Director Simon Beecroft

For Lucasfilm
Executive Editor J. W. Rinzler
Art Director Troy Alders
Story Group Leland Chee, Pablo Hidalgo
and Rayne Roberts

First published in Great Britain in 2016
by Dorling Kindersley Limited
80 Strand, London, WC2R 0RL

Contains content previously published in *Star Wars The Force
Awakens: The Visual Dictionary* (2015), *Beware the Sith* (2012),
Battles for the Galaxy (2011) and *Mysteries of the Jedi* (2011)

Page design Copyright © 2016 Dorling Kindersley Limited
A Penguin Random House Company

001–297038–04/16

© & TM 2016 LUCASFILM LTD.

A CIP catalogue record for this book is
available from the British Library.

ISBN: 978-0-2412-7585-6

Printed and bound in China

The publisher would like to thank Chris Trevas and
Chris Reiff for their artwork on pages 14–15 and Julia March
and Victoria Taylor for their editorial work.

www.dk.com
www.starwars.com

A WORLD OF IDEAS:
SEE ALL THERE IS TO KNOW

CONTENTS

THE FORCE HAS TWO SIDES

THE FORCE IS AN invisible energy that flows through all living things. Studying the Force will grant you knowledge and power. You must use this power wisely, or face the consequences.

THE LIGHT SIDE

The Jedi study the light side of the Force and use their wisdom to uphold justice and protect the innocent. Using the Force allows Jedi to live in harmony with the galaxy, feel things before they see them, react quickly to danger and use a lightsaber with incredible skill.

- **BRAVERY**

- **WISDOM**

- **LOYALTY**

- **INNER STRENGTH**

- **JUSTICE**

PASSION ■

FORBIDDEN KNOWLEDGE ■

FREEDOM ■

GREAT STRENGTH ■

RAW POWER ■

THE DARK SIDE

The Sith study the dark side of the Force, which feeds on negative feelings such as anger, fear and jealousy. The dark side offers almost unlimited power and access to dangerous knowledge, but at a terrible price. Submitting to the dark side transforms the Sith into something so evil, they cease to be human.

WHICH WOULD YOU CHOOSE?

THE JEDI CODE

Welcome to the Jedi Order. As a Jedi you will learn to harness great power – but you must never use it for personal gain. To live the life of a Jedi, you will need to follow the Jedi Code. It explains the path you must take to become powerful yet remain selfless. The Jedi way of life rests on three basic principles: self-discipline, knowledge and the Force.

SELF-DISCIPLINE

Your role as a Jedi must come before your own desires. That means having no possessions and not becoming emotionally attached: if a Jedi cares more for something or someone than he does about his mission, he might make a poor decision and jeopardise the safety of the galaxy.

THE FORCE

A Jedi must study the Force and live in tune with it. You must be able to control the Force, communicate with it and know its will. When you interact with the Force, you will possess great power. But you must use it wisely.

KNOWLEDGE

As a Jedi, you will value knowledge and wisdom in yourself and others. You must learn how to distinguish truth from lies, and how to seek out information so you can solve problems and resolve conflict.

"THERE IS NO EMOTION, THERE IS PEACE.
THERE IS NO IGNORANCE, THERE IS KNOWLEDGE.
THERE IS NO PASSION, THERE IS SERENITY.
THERE IS NO CHAOS, THERE IS HARMONY.
THERE IS NO DEATH, THERE IS THE FORCE."

FORCE JUMP

CHANNEL THROUGH: Full body
BEST FOR: Leaping out of harm's
way; quick movement during a
duel; surprising enemies
from a great height.
LEARN FROM: Yoda, who evades
his enemies during a duel with
multiple Force jumps.
DANGER LEVEL: Moderate

USING THE FORCE

The Force might
be invisible, but it can
be channeled through a
Jedi's body for a range
of different results.

FORCE DEFLECTION

CHANNEL THROUGH: Hands
BEST FOR: Shielding yourself from incoming attacks.
LEARN FROM: Yoda, who repulses deadly Sith lightning
fired at him by Chancellor Palpatine.
DANGER LEVEL: High

FORCE PILOTING

CHANNEL THROUGH:
Hands and eyes
BEST FOR: Steering
through busy airways.
LEARN FROM: Anakin, who
flies safely at super
speed above Coruscant.
DANGER LEVEL: High

FEEL THE FORCE

THE FORCE IS AN ENERGY FIELD that flows through
every living thing and is accessible to those with the
right mindset and training. Jedi spend many years
studying how to apply its many uses without causing
harm to themselves or others. Do you seek advice?
Are you being attacked? The Force can help.

TELEKINESIS

CHANNEL THROUGH: Hands
BEST FOR: Moving objects without touching them; summoning your lightsaber.
LEARN FROM: Yoda, who uses the Force to stop heavy objects from crushing himself and others during his battle with Count Dooku.
DANGER LEVEL: Moderate

BEAST CONTROL

CHANNEL THROUGH: Hands and mind
BEST FOR: Taming wild beasts that threaten your safety.
LEARN FROM: Anakin, who takes control of a particularly vicious reek in the execution arena on Geonosis.
DANGER LEVEL: High

FORCE GHOST

CHANNEL THROUGH: Spirit
BEST FOR: Living on after death to advise and guide others.
LEARN FROM: Obi-Wan, who becomes one with the Force after sacrificing himself on the Death Star.
DANGER LEVEL: Low, but only possible for a few rare Jedi.

FORCE DISTURBANCE

CHANNEL THROUGH: Heart and mind
BEST FOR: Sensing disturbances in the Force; letting you know what is happening elsewhere in the galaxy.
LEARN FROM: Yoda, who senses the start of the Jedi Purge.
DANGER LEVEL: Low

SITH COMBAT

The Sith use the dark side of the Force to fight viciously. Force choking weakens or kills through strangulation. Count Dooku uses it to attack Obi-Wan Kenobi. Force lightning is deadly blue crackling energy. These cruel uses of the Force are forbidden for Jedi.

JEDI MIND TRICK

CHANNEL THROUGH: Hands and mind
BEST FOR: Persuading others to leave you alone or to do what you want.
LEARN FROM: Obi-Wan, who convinces a stormtrooper patrol to let him pass through a checkpoint at Mos Eisley.
DANGER LEVEL: Low, but mind tricks work only on the weak-minded. A Jedi must be very careful not to abuse this power.

HOW CAN YOU BECOME A JEDI?

YOUNGLING

Not everyone can become a Jedi: it requires dedication, hard work and a sensitivity to the Force. It can take more than 20 years of training and there are several stages to go through. If you show promise and are selected, your Jedi career starts here. Good luck!

YOUNGLING

Great news! You have been selected to train as a Jedi. You will start as a Youngling and will live in the Jedi Temple, where you will study the basics of the Force. Most Jedi begin their training when they are babies, but some successful Jedi have started later. Get ready to work hard!

JEDI COUNCIL

The Jedi Council is made up of 12 Jedi, who are in charge of running the Jedi Order. They resolve disputes, make decisions and uphold the Jedi Code.

GRAND MASTER
YODA

GRAND MASTER

You'll have to be right at the top of your game to reach this rank. As Grand Master, Yoda is the head of not just the Jedi High Council, but the whole Order. Along with other Council members, he selects who will become Younglings.

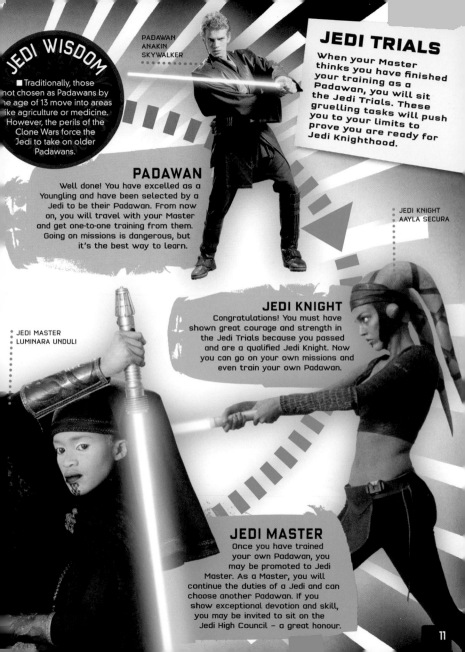

PADAWAN ANAKIN SKYWALKER

JEDI TRIALS

When your Master thinks you have finished your training as a Padawan, you will sit the Jedi Trials. These gruelling tasks will push you to your limits to prove you are ready for Jedi Knighthood.

PADAWAN

Well done! You have excelled as a Youngling and have been selected by a Jedi to be their Padawan. From now on, you will travel with your Master and get one-to-one training from them. Going on missions is dangerous, but it's the best way to learn.

JEDI KNIGHT AAYLA SECURA

JEDI KNIGHT

Congratulations! You must have shown great courage and strength in the Jedi Trials because you passed and are a qualified Jedi Knight. Now you can go on your own missions and even train your own Padawan.

JEDI MASTER LUMINARA UNDULI

JEDI MASTER

Once you have trained your own Padawan, you may be promoted to Jedi Master. As a Master, you will continue the duties of a Jedi and can choose another Padawan. If you show exceptional devotion and skill, you may be invited to sit on the Jedi High Council – a great honour.

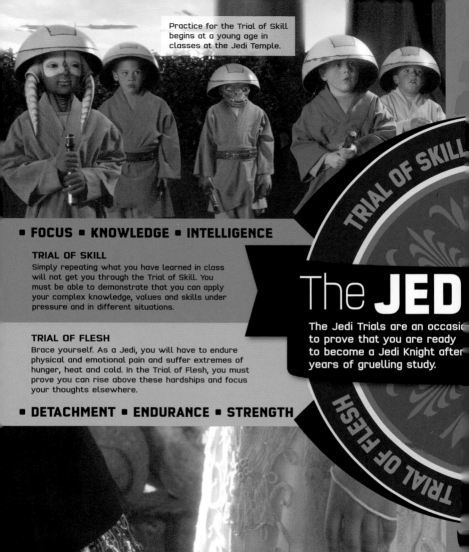

Practice for the Trial of Skill begins at a young age in classes at the Jedi Temple.

• FOCUS • KNOWLEDGE • INTELLIGENCE

TRIAL OF SKILL

Simply repeating what you have learned in class will not get you through the Trial of Skill. You must be able to demonstrate that you can apply your complex knowledge, values and skills under pressure and in different situations.

TRIAL OF FLESH

Brace yourself. As a Jedi, you will have to endure physical and emotional pain and suffer extremes of hunger, heat and cold. In the Trial of Flesh, you must prove you can rise above these hardships and focus your thoughts elsewhere.

• DETACHMENT • ENDURANCE • STRENGTH

The JEDI

The Jedi Trials are an occasion to prove that you are ready to become a Jedi Knight after years of gruelling study.

TRIAL OF FLESH

Anakin experiences his Trial of Flesh when he loses part of his arm, including his hand, in combat with Count Dooku. From then on, he has a mechanical hand.

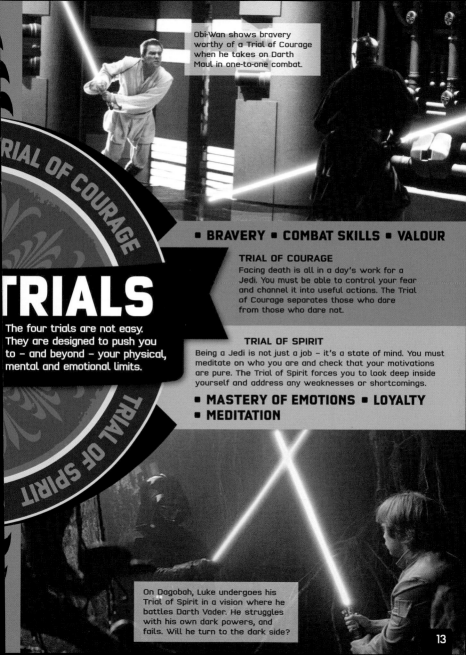

Obi-Wan shows bravery worthy of a Trial of Courage when he takes on Darth Maul in one-to-one combat.

TRIALS

The four trials are not easy. They are designed to push you to – and beyond – your physical, mental and emotional limits.

• BRAVERY • COMBAT SKILLS • VALOUR

TRIAL OF COURAGE

Facing death is all in a day's work for a Jedi. You must be able to control your fear and channel it into useful actions. The Trial of Courage separates those who dare from those who dare not.

TRIAL OF SPIRIT

Being a Jedi is not just a job – it's a state of mind. You must meditate on who you are and check that your motivations are pure. The Trial of Spirit forces you to look deep inside yourself and address any weaknesses or shortcomings.

• MASTERY OF EMOTIONS • LOYALTY • MEDITATION

On Dagobah, Luke undergoes his Trial of Spirit in a vision where he battles Darth Vader. He struggles with his own dark powers, and fails. Will he turn to the dark side?

HOW TO BUILD A LIGHTSABER

THE LIGHTSABER is an ancient sword known for its elegance as well as its power in battle. It is the weapon of choice for both the Jedi and their enemies, the Sith. Lightsabers consist of a handle, or "hilt", that emits a coloured blade of plasma energy. As part of their training, every Jedi learns how to build their own lightsaber. All lightsabers contain these eight basic parts, but you can vary the design to suit your own taste and needs.

MAIN HILT ■

The plasma for the blade is created here in the blade energy channel from a special type of gas.

■ BLADE EMITTER

This is where the plasma blade beams out. The metal ring houses the base of the blade and makes sure it keeps its cylindrical shape.

CRYSTAL

A crystal sits at the heart of every lightsaber and gives the blade its bright colour. Most Jedi lightsabers glow blue or green because they use crystals mined on the planet Ilum. The Sith prefer to make their own artificial crystals so their blades glow a more fearsome red color.

The crystal also determines the length of the blade. Having more than one crystal means you can vary the length of your blade. Many Jedi believe that three is best number of crystals to have.

FOCUSING LENS ■

The focusing lens channels the plasma for the blade and makes sure it has a fixed end point. Most blades are one metre (3¼ feet) long, but they can vary.

BLADE ENERGY CHANNEL

14

POWER CELL ■

Energy from special diatium batteries stored in the power cell heats up gas to create plasma for the blade.

POMMEL CAP ■

The pommel seals the end of the lightsaber. It often contains a back-up battery. If you want, you can add a ring that clips to your belt.

■ CONTROLS

Buttons activate the blade, but Jedi who are very skilled in the Force can control these things using the Force instead.

ENERGY
GATE

BUTTON ADJUSTS
BLADE'S LENGTH

BUTTON ADJUSTS
BLADE'S POWER
SETTING

■ HANDGRIP

This outer part of the hilt is covered in ridges so that the lightsaber doesn't fly out of your hand while you are swinging it around.

DOS AND DON'TS

■ Don't plunge your blade into water – it will sizzle out unless it has been specially adapted to work underwater.

■ Take care of your lightsaber – if you lose it, it can take a month to build a new one.

■ Make sure your power cell is covered with an inert power insulator, otherwise you could get electrocuted!

■ Keep fit: the forces acting on the weightless blade mean that a lightsaber requires strong arms to control it.

■ Study the Force: anyone can wield a lightsaber, but only those with Force powers can unlock its true potential.

■ Be careful: the blade can slice through almost anything. (Any injuries you get won't bleed because the blade is so hot it seals the skin, but that doesn't mean they won't hurt!)

■ Keep your lightsaber in good condition and it could last forever and never run out of power.

Mace's hilt is plated with golden electrum metal – a decoration reserved for senior Jedi.

Mace chooses a rare crystal that emits a violet glow.

Anakin Skywalker's Lightsaber

Mace Windu's Lightsaber

Luke Skywalker's Lightsaber

This lightsaber is passed from Anakin to Luke. It is lost when Luke fights Darth Vader on Cloud City.

After Luke loses his first lightsaber fighting Darth Vader, he builds a new one using notes left by Obi-Wan.

Younglings practice with safety blades. The power set is very low to avoid injuries.

"Your lightsaber is ... YOUR LIFE!"

OBI-WAN TO ANAKIN

The Sith Darth Maul chooses saberstaff, which is double-bladed. These are harder to use, but some Sith favor them because they loo more menacing and allow a mor aggressive style of comba

Darth Maul's Lightsaber

As a mark of respect for his Master, Obi-Wan bases the design of his lightsaber on Qui-Gon's.

Obi-Wan Kenobi's Lightsaber

Qui-Gon Jinn's Lightsaber

A single large power cell is common. However, Qui-Gon is so advanced, he can build a complex system of smaller power cells that are placed within the ridges of his handgrip.

Yoda's Lightsaber

A smaller hilt and shorter blade are perfectly sized for Yoda.

LIGHTSABER SPOTTING

JEDI WISDOM

■ Jedi lightsabers use natural crystals that usually glow blue or green. The Sith use synthetic crystals which glow red; a more menacing colour.

EVERY LIGHTSABER IS handmade by its owner, so there is a dazzling array of variations. A Jedi or Sith can customise the handle, controls, size and colour according to their needs and their tastes.

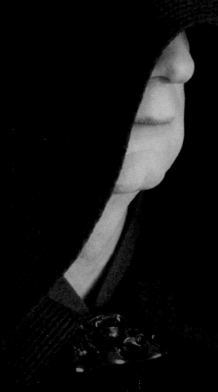

THE DARK SIDE

Fear and mystery surround the dark side of the Force. Whispered stories and strange rumours are all that is known about the Sith and their deadly powers. The Sith rule from the shadows, using their terrible powers to shroud the galaxy in darkness and bend others to their will. There is only one way to discover all the secrets of the dark side – by joining the Sith.

TERRIFYING POWER

RUTHLESS AMBITION

SECRET TEACHINGS

UNSPEAKABLE EVIL

THE SITH CODE

Peace is a lie, there is only passion.
Through passion, I gain strength.
Through strength, I gain power.
Through power, I gain victory.
Through victory, my chains are broken.
The Force shall free me.

19

The Rule
OF TWO

In the past, there were many Sith. They studied the Force and grew powerful – but they also became suspicious of each other. Fighting broke out among them and the Sith Order was greatly weakened. The Rule of Two was introduced to prevent the power of the dark side from destroying the Order.

POWER HUNGRY

The Rule of Two states that there can be only one Sith Master and only one apprentice at any time. When the apprentice grows more powerful than his Master, he is to destroy him and choose an apprentice of his own. But the Rule of Two has a flaw: the Sith Code encourages passion and ambition – not loyalty. As long as the Sith exist, there will always be a brutal struggle for power.

SITH SECRETS

■ Darth Bane was a Sith Lord who lived over 1,000 years ago. He became dissatisfied with his Sith brotherhood and created his own Sith Order, in which he instituted the Rule of Two.

APPRENTICE'S APPRENTICE
Many Sith apprentices don't obey the Rule of Two and secretly take on their own apprentices. Sidious began training Darth Maul before he had destroyed his own Master, Darth Plagueis. Darth Tyranus trained Asajj Ventress and Savage Opress while he was Sidious's apprentice, and Darth Vader had a secret apprentice called Galen Marek.

EXPENDABLE APPRENTICE
Darth Tyranus is Sidious's second apprentice, but he is needed only until Sidious succeeds in turning Anakin Skywalker to the dark side. Sidious does not expect Tyranus's powers to eclipse his own, and plans to have Tyranus destroyed when the time is right.

UNWANTED APPRENTICE
Darth Sidious watched Anakin for years before the Jedi became his Sith apprentice. But Darth Vader was gravely wounded by Obi-Wan on the volcano planet Mustafar, so he now feels trapped in his armoured body. Vader is no longer the apprentice that Sidious hoped he would be.

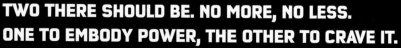

" TWO THERE SHOULD BE. NO MORE, NO LESS. ONE TO EMBODY POWER, THE OTHER TO CRAVE IT.

DARTH BANE

Sith
LIGHTSABERS

The Sith possess enough Force power to battle without a lightsaber, but each new apprentice chooses his own weapon as part of his training. Sith lightsabers are powered by synthetic red crystals, which emit a strong crimson blade – reflecting the Sith's passion, bloodlust and rage.

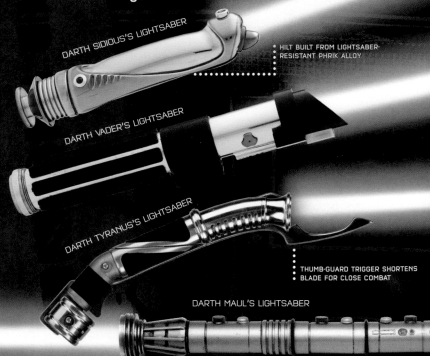

DARTH SIDIOUS'S LIGHTSABER

HILT BUILT FROM LIGHTSABER-RESISTANT PHRIK ALLOY

DARTH VADER'S LIGHTSABER

DARTH TYRANUS'S LIGHTSABER

THUMB-GUARD TRIGGER SHORTENS BLADE FOR CLOSE COMBAT

DARTH MAUL'S LIGHTSABER

Darth Sidious's ornate aurodium-plated lightsaber hilt reflects his passion for dark objects of antiquity. Its rounded form allows for fluid movement in combat.

Darth Vader's black-alloy lightsaber closely resembles the style of his Jedi weapon. To fit his mechanical hands, however, Vader's lightsaber hilt is larger than normal.

Darth Tyranus uses the same lightsaber he built when he was a Jedi. Its curved hilt is designed for precise handling. When Tyranus became a Sith, Sidious gave him a new red crystal to replace his green blade.

Darth Maul finds a single-bladed lightsaber limiting in combat. His saberstaff is perfect for attacking two opponents at once, but its size means that Maul has to be more acrobatic in battle.

SITH POWERS

As a member of the Order of the Sith, you will learn to harness the power of the dark side. These powers are deadly and unpredictable – but when used correctly, they are almost unstoppable.

If you are cornered by a Jedi Knight, or come face to face with a threatening bounty hunter, call on the dark side of the Force. But remember: using these powers can be extremely dangerous.

FORCE CLOUDING

CHANNEL THROUGH: Mind
SITH EXPERT: Darth Sidious can cloud the Force so completely, the Jedi remain unaware of his Sith identity.
DANGER LEVEL: Low – unless discovered!

MIND CONTROL

CHANNEL THROUGH: Mind
SITH EXPERT: Darth Tyranus can control the minds of most of his enemies – although some Jedi are able to resist.
DANGER LEVEL: Moderate

FORCE CHOKE

CHANNEL THROUGH: Hands
SITH EXPERT: Darth Vader can use the Force to strangle his victims without touching them.
DANGER LEVEL: Moderate

POWER OVER DEATH

CHANNEL THROUGH: Body and mind
SITH EXPERT: Darth Sidious uses his dark side powers to extend his life and to save Anakin from certain death.
DANGER LEVEL: High

SITH LIGHTNING

CHANNEL THROUGH: Hands
SITH EXPERT: Darth Sidious can emit intense bolts of deadly lightning for extended periods of time.
DANGER LEVEL: High

TELEKINESIS

CHANNEL THROUGH: Hands and arms
SITH EXPERT: Darth Tyranus can move extremely heavy objects with very little effort.
DANGER LEVEL: Moderate

FORBIDDEN KNOWLEDGE

CHANNEL THROUGH: Mind
SITH EXPERT: Darth Sidious claims to know the dangerous secret of immortality
DANGER LEVEL: High

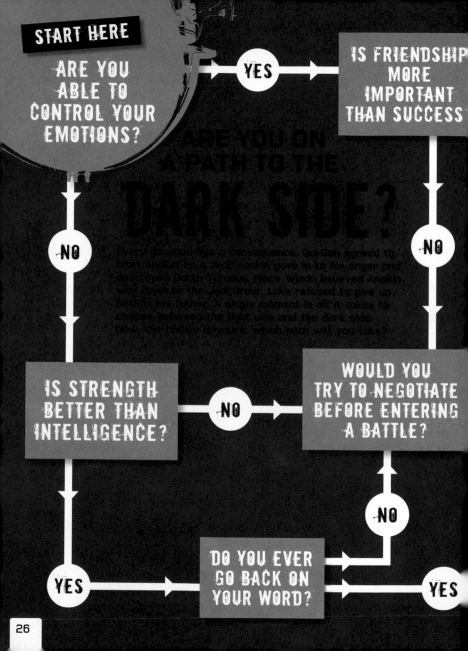

ARE YOU ABLE TO CONTROL YOUR EMOTIONS?

YES

IS FRIENDSHIP MORE IMPORTANT THAN SUCCESS

ARE YOU ON A PATH TO THE

DARK SIDE?

Every decision has a consequence. Qui-Gon agreed to train Anakin to be a Jedi. Anakin gave in to his anger and destroyed Darth Tyranus. Mace Windu believed Anakin was loyal to the Jedi Order. Luke refused to give up faith in his father. A single moment is all it takes to choose between the light side and the dark side. Now, the choice is yours: which path will you take?

NO

NO

IS STRENGTH BETTER THAN INTELLIGENCE?

NO

WOULD YOU TRY TO NEGOTIATE BEFORE ENTERING A BATTLE?

NO

DO YOU EVER GO BACK ON YOUR WORD?

YES

YES

26

YES →

DO YOU VALUE POWER MORE THAN JUSTICE?

→ **NO** →

JEDI
You are brave and selfless enough to defend the galaxy from evil! Stay strong – and beware the Sith.

YES →

SENATOR
You have the chance to make a real difference in the galaxy through discussion and cooperation. Make sure you do not become greedy under the influence of others.

BOUNTY HUNTER
You always look out for yourself – and will be very rich. Just be careful who you choose to work for.

YES

NO

NO →

SITH
You are strong and ambitious. You have chosen to seek power at all costs. But remember, the dark side will change you into something horrible.

DO YOU CRAVE POWER MORE THAN RICHES?

→ **YES**

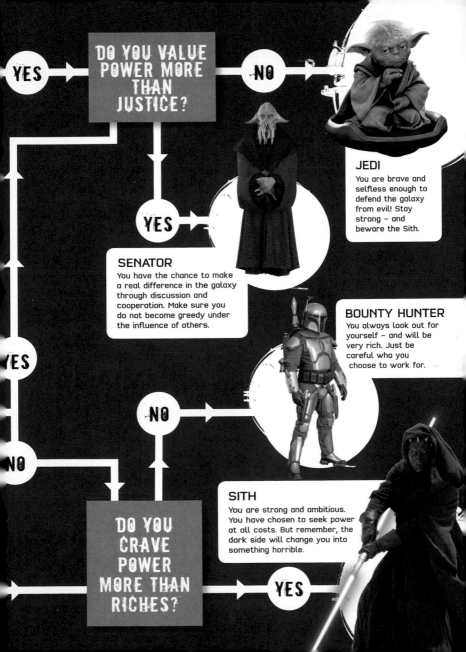

DROID ARMY STATS

LEADER: COUNT DOOKU
ALLEGIANCE: SEPARATISTS
HEADQUARTERS: GEONOSIS
WEAPONS: BLASTER RIFLE, BLASTER PISTOL, THERMAL DETONATOR
VEHICLES: STAP, MTT, AAT, DROID TRI-FIGHTER
VALUES: OBEDIENCE TO PROGRAMMING

CHAIN OF COMMAND

DARTH SIDIOUS (IN SECRET)

COUNT DOOKU

GENERAL GRIEVOUS

COMMANDER BATTLE DROIDS

BATTLE DROIDS

Super battle droids have thick armour and blasters built into their arms. They aren't as common as regular battle droids but they are much harder to destroy.

RADIATION SENSORS TO SEE IN THE DARK

SUPER BATTLE DROID

TWIN RAPID-FIRE BLASTER CANNONS

DROIDEKAS

DROIDEKAS LOOK LIKE THEIR INSECTOID ALIEN BUILDERS

DEADLY ROLLERS

Droidekas, or destroyer droids, have their own shield generators. They can also transform into a wheel and roll toward a target. They are so fast and powerful, they sometimes make Jedi Knights retreat!

**BATTLE
DROID**

DROID IS
DIRECTED
FROM CENTRAL
COMMAND SIGNAL

E-5 BLASTER

Droid
ARMY

FRAGILE
CONSTRUCTION

The Separatists use droid
soldiers to fight their battles.
Droids never get tired, always
obey orders and can be easily
replaced when damaged. Battle
droids, super battle droids and
droidekas may not be very
clever, but they can be deadly!

EXPENDABLE
B1 battle droids are
the Separatists' foot
soldiers. They are
easy to defeat but
can be dangerous if
many attack at once.
Droid commanders
have yellow markings
and are slightly more
independently minded.

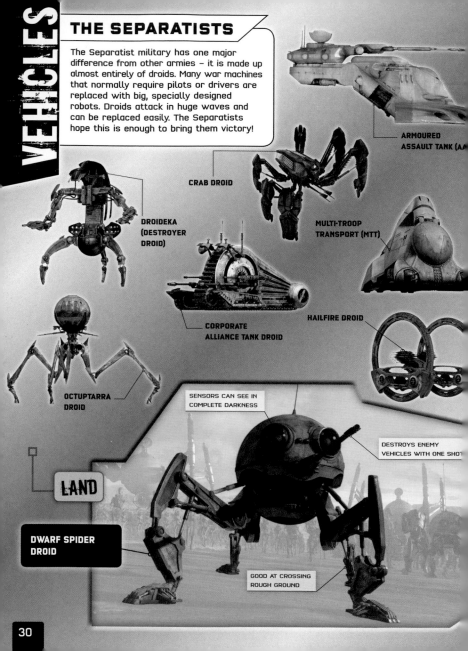

THE SEPARATISTS

The Separatist military has one major difference from other armies – it is made up almost entirely of droids. Many war machines that normally require pilots or drivers are replaced with big, specially designed robots. Droids attack in huge waves and can be replaced easily. The Separatists hope this is enough to bring them victory!

ARMOURED ASSAULT TANK (AA

CRAB DROID

DROIDEKA (DESTROYER DROID)

MULTI-TROOP TRANSPORT (MTT)

CORPORATE ALLIANCE TANK DROID

HAILFIRE DROID

OCTUPTARRA DROID

SENSORS CAN SEE IN COMPLETE DARKNESS

DESTROYS ENEMY VEHICLES WITH ONE SHOT

LAND

DWARF SPIDER DROID

GOOD AT CROSSING ROUGH GROUND

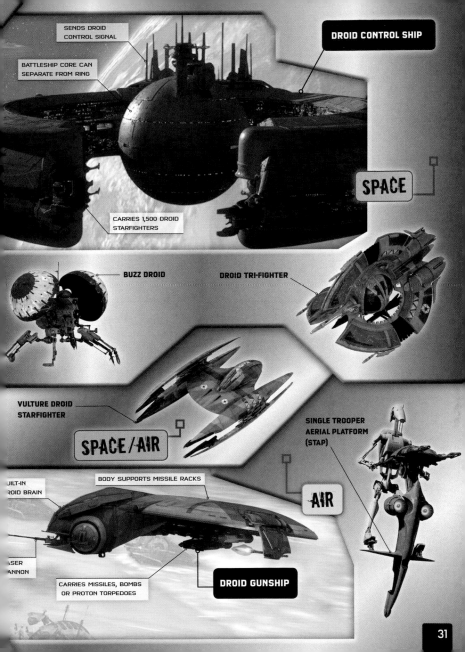

SENDS DROID
CONTROL SIGNAL

DROID CONTROL SHIP

BATTLESHIP CORE CAN
SEPARATE FROM RING

SPACE

CARRIES 1,500 DROID
STARFIGHTERS

BUZZ DROID

DROID TRI-FIGHTER

VULTURE DROID
STARFIGHTER

SINGLE TROOPER
AERIAL PLATFORM
(STAP)

SPACE / AIR

AIR

UILT-IN
ROID BRAIN

BODY SUPPORTS MISSILE RACKS

ASER
ANNON

CARRIES MISSILES, BOMBS
OR PROTON TORPEDOES

DROID GUNSHIP

clone ARMY

BUILT-IN COMLINK

DC-15 BLASTER RIFLE

The Republic doesn't have a military unit of its own, so finding a ready-made army of clone fighters on Kamino seems too good to be true! As the Jedi Generals lead their new soldiers into battle against the Separatists, they don't realise that their troopers are secretly loyal to Darth Sidious.

The clone army is equipped with starfighters, tanks, speeders and warships. On Coruscant, thousands of clones march into troop carriers on their way to fight the Separatists.

PHASE I ARMOUR

ARMOUR HAS 20 SEPARATE PIECES

RESTRICTIVE ARMOUR
The early clone troopers wore Phase I armour with its distinctive helmet fin and pure white colour. Made of plastoid, the armour provided protection against explosions and shrapnel, but it wasn't very easy to move around in. It was soon replaced with Phase II armour.

CHAIN OF COMMAND
CHANCELLOR PALPATINE

JEDI GENERALS

CLONE COMMANDERS

CLONE CAPTAINS

CLONE LIEUTENANTS

CLONE SERGEANTS

CLONE TROOPERS

BORN TO FIGHT

Each clone is grown from the DNA of the bounty hunter
Jango Fett. Clones are designed to age twice as fast as
normal humans and are trained for a life of combat.

PHASE II ARMOUR

POUCHES
CONTAIN MEDICAL
KIT AND EXTRA
AMMUNITION

DC-15A BLASTER
FIRES 500 SHOTS
FROM A SINGLE
GAS CARTRIDGE

ARMOUR HAS
SPECIAL
ANTI-BLASTER
COATING

▶RMOUR UPDATES

▶ Phase II armour
▶esigned with
▶rovements
▶rned from battle
▶erience. It is
▶e comfortable,
▶nds up to blaster
▶ and comes in
▶houflage colours
▶en required.

33

Clone Trooper
IDENTIFICATION

You can't win a war without adapting to changing circumstances. At the start of the Clone Wars, every trooper wore identical armour. But as the fighting spread to hundreds of planets, clone armour became customised to get the job done better. Colour markings now denote unit affiliation, while extra equipment or design adjustments adapt the armour to suit the needs of individual missions.

CLONE TROOP
Basic clone trooper armou is plain white blaster resistc However, it is not always suitable for working in extreme environments or handling specialised equipment.

CLONE COMMANDERS

COMMANDER NEYO
Leader of the 91st Reconnaissance Corps, Neyo is an expert BARC speeder pilot. His helmet has been adjusted so it is extra streamlined.

COMMANDER BLY
Bly serves with the Star Corps. The viewfinder on his helmet provides better visibility in the jungles of Felucia.

COMMANDER CODY
The troopers of the 2 Attack Battalion repo Cody, who stays in co with built-in radio ante

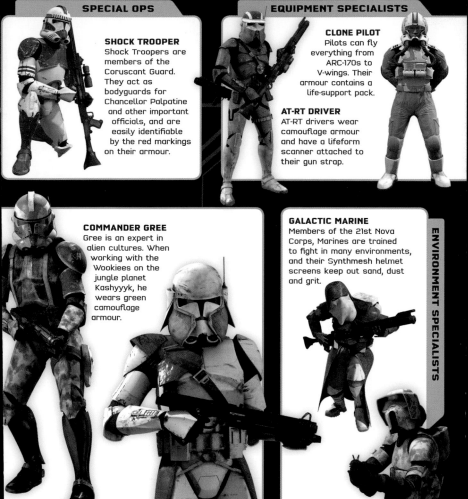

SHOCK TROOPER
Shock Troopers are members of the Coruscant Guard. They act as bodyguards for Chancellor Palpatine and other important officials, and are easily identifiable by the red markings on their armour.

CLONE PILOT
Pilots can fly everything from ARC-170s to V-wings. Their armour contains a life-support pack.

AT-RT DRIVER
AT-RT drivers wear camouflage armour and have a lifeform scanner attached to their gun strap.

COMMANDER GREE
Gree is an expert in alien cultures. When working with the Wookiees on the jungle planet Kashyyyk, he wears green camouflage armour.

GALACTIC MARINE
Members of the 21st Nova Corps, Marines are trained to fight in many environments, and their Synthmesh helmet screens keep out sand, dust and grit.

COMMANDER BACARA
Bacara is one of the leaders of the ctic Marines. He wears the maroon s of the Marines, and a protective around his waist to indicate rank.

SWAMP TROOPER
With lightweight, camouflaged armour, swamp troopers can operate on soggy planets where heavy equipment would just sink into mud.

35

THE REPUBLIC

During the Clone Wars, enormous Republic assault ships and cruisers transport thousands of Jedi and clone forces to battlefields across the galaxy. Walkers, tanks, starfighters and gunships are commanded by clones on land, in the sky and in space! The Jedi have powerful vessels, too; their ships are fast and nimble.

ALL TERRAIN TACTICAL ENFORCER (AT-TE)

SWAMP SPEEDER

ALL TERRAIN OPEN TRANSPORT (AT-OT)

CLONE TURBO TANK

ALL TERRAIN ATTACK POD (AT-AP)

ALL TERRAIN RECON TRANSPORT (AT-RT)

LAND

TURBOLASER DESTROYS ESCAPING STARSHIPS

WEAPON CAN BE REPLACED WITH ION CANNON OR MISSILE LAUNCHER

CLONE COMMANDERS WATCH BATTLEFIELD AND GIVE ORDERS

THICK ARMOUR

SELF-PROPELLED HEAVY ARTILLERY-TURBOLASER (SPHA-T)

12 LEGS PROVIDE STABILITY

REPUBLIC GUNSHIP

COCKPIT

GUNSHIPS ARE NOT HEAVILY ARMED AND TRY TO AVOID ENEMY FIRE

CLONE GUNNERS TRACK THEIR TARGETS

FORWARD LASER

BIKER ADVANCED RECON COMMANDO (BARC) SPEEDER

AIR

470 STARFIGHTER

REPUBLIC ASSAULT SHIP

REPUBLIC ATTACK CRUISER

JEDI INTERCEPTOR

SPACE

ASTROMECH DROID REPAIRS DAMAGE

JEDI STARFIGHTER

PACT SIZE

ION CANNON KNOCKS OUT ENEMY SHIP'S ELECTRONICS

S-FOIL WING PANEL

REPUBLIC CRUISER

Clone Trooper to
STORMTROOPER

The helmet has a T-shaped visor th closely resemble one worn by Jang Fett. It also has a fin on top.

The Clone Wars are over. The Republic is now an oppressive Empire and Chancellor Palpatine has taken control as Emperor. And he doesn't have to look far to find an army to do his bidding. With only a few modifications, the Republic's clone troopers are swiftly transformed into Imperial stormtroopers. Their mission may have changed from defeating Separatists to destroying Rebels, but these troopers have always stayed loyal to their commander.

Each trooper carries a standard issue DC-15A blaster rifle which can fire up to 500 shots on a single ammo pack.

JANGO FETT

This deadly bounty hunter caught the attention of Count Dooku, who hired him to be the source of the genetic material used to create the clones. Jango also helped train the clones, and their armour – especially the Phase I design – is clearly based on Jango's Mandalorian battle armour.

Rocket backpack also contains a missile

Gauntlet can spray fire at enemies

ORIGINS OF THE CLONE

Phase I armour is made up of a black bodysuit, surrounded by c 20-piece blaster resistant shell. Commanders ha yellow markings

PHASE I CLONE TROOPER

Early clone troopers wear identical white armour – except for commanders, who have coloured markings. This armour is bulky and uncomfortable for long-term combat.

The new helmet includes an advanced air filtration system, while the visor contains a targeting system and screen that displays important information.

The helmet is now fully sealed and can supply emergency air for 20 minutes. Some troopers complain about the smaller eyeholes.

The DC-15A blaster rifle is still in use, but troopers also carry special weapons if needed.

Stormtroopers carry the E-11 blaster rifle. On its automatic setting, it fires blaster bolts at an extremely high rate of speed.

This armour can survive explosions and blaster hits, and the foot casing can be magnetised. Phase II armour is easily personalised to denote unit affiliation, or painted in camouflage colours.

Stormtrooper armour consists of only 18 blaster-resistant pieces, surrounding a black bodysuit that can adapt to extreme temperatures.

PHASE II CLONE TROOPER

Battlefield experience in the Clone Wars leads to Phase II armour. It is more flexible and comfortable. Troopers often adapt or paint their armour for particular missions.

IMPERIAL STORMTROOPER

To symbolise the purity of the new Empire, stormtrooper armour returns to the all-white colouration of the earliest clones. The look inspires fear across the galaxy!

REPUBLIC FIGHTER

The ARC-170 is a heavy starfighter often used as a bomber. It only takes an ARC-170, two pilots, a gunner and an astromech droid to make enemies turn and run!

ASSAULT SHIPS

Some starfighters can do everything from bombing to dogfighting. Certain features of the Republic's ARC-170 were incorporated into the Rebel Alliance's famous X-wing.

REBEL FAVOURITE

The X-wing is a sturdy one-pilot ship, but it still uses an astromech. It offers a good balance of speed and firepower, and is equipped with two proton torpedoes.

WARTIME
TRANSFORMATION

War can destroy, but it can also create. In order to gain an edge over their enemies, armies invent new technologies and designs to improve their starships and ground vehicles. Between the final days of the Republic and the fall of the Empire, the vehicles of combat became better and better, even though their basic shapes remained the same.

REPUBLIC MACHINE

This six-legged AT-TE walker is difficult to knock over and can even climb up cliff faces. It is packed with weapons, but can be destroyed by enemy cannons.

HEAVY WALKERS

Clone troopers used walkers to smash Separatist tanks during the Clone Wars. The design worked so well that the Empire built its own deadly walkers.

IMPERIAL MONSTE

The fearsome AT-AT towers over other war machines. I less stable than the AT-TE much tougher and scarier.

REPUBLIC SCOUT

The AT-RT is a small scouting vehicle that gives its driver a high vantage point to scan the territory, but it also makes him an easy target.

SCOUT WALKERS

The Republic army used two-legged walkers for fast scouting of unfamiliar terrain. The Imperial Army improved the design by adding more protection for the walker's drivers.

IMPERIAL THREAT

The Imperial AT-ST is taller than the AT-RT and its cockpit is completely enclosed. It is better armed as well, so keep clear – for your own safety!

REPUBLIC STAR

The Jedi Interceptor carries an astromech droid and is so small and manoeuvrable that it's hard to hit! Due to its compact size, it needs a hyperspace ring for long-distance travel.

INTERCEPTORS

The Jedi Interceptor was small, lightweight and fast. Some parts of its design were used in Imperial TIE fighters, while others were incorporated into the Rebel Alliance's trusty A-wing.

REBEL SPEEDSTER

The A-wing doesn't have an astromech droid, but it does have a built-in hyperdrive engine for quick escapes. Rebel pilots love its speed!

REPUBLIC POWER

The Republic Attack Cruiser carries starfighters, walkers and up to 2,000 soldiers. It can land directly on planets to unload its troops while giving covering fire.

DESTROYERS

In the Clone Wars, these huge ships carried clone troops. After installing more weapons, the Empire used Star Destroyers to smash Rebel battleships and conquer entire planets.

IMPERIAL MIGHT

The Imperial Star Destroyer is bigger than the Attack Cruiser and can't land on planets. But it can destroy targets from space with its turbolasers – and it carries squadrons of TIE fighters.

REVIEWING THE TROOPS

As the Emperor's right-hand man, Darth Vader outranks most officers. The Sith Lord has the power to command legions of stormtroopers and has his own ship – the Super Star Destroyer – *Executor*.

Stormtroopers are a special branch of the Imperial forces, and most of them are clones. The Imperial military also includes army and navy troopers, TIE fighter pilots, AT-AT drivers and the Emperor's red-robed Royal Guard.

Imperial ARMY

The Empire has one of the most powerful militaries in the history of the galaxy. Well-equipped and well-trained, there are thousands of stormtroopers, starships and vehicles ready to invade troublesome planets. The Imperial Army is confident it will crush the Rebellion, soon.

CHAIN OF COMMAND

EMPEROR PALPATINE

GRAND MOFFS

GENERALS/ADMIRALS

IMPERIAL OFFICERS

STORMTROOPERS

CLONE TO STORM

Clone troopers became stormtroopers when the Clone Wars ended with Order 66. Specialty units such as snowtroopers, sandtroopers and scout troopers are easily recognised by distinctive armour.

IMPERIAL STORMTROOPER

HELMET CONTAINS TARGETING EQUIPMENT

INSIGNIA SHOWS HIGH RANK

GRAND MOFF TARKIN

SUPERIOR

Grand Moff Tarkin is in charge of the Death Star project and has served the Emperor since the beginning. Cruel and power-hungry, he is one of the few Imperial officials with enough authority to give orders to Darth Vader!

THE EMPIRE

The Empire's starships and vehicles are designed to make enemies run in terror! The mighty AT-AT walker shakes the ground as it moves and TIE fighter engines make an eerie wailing sound. Smaller Imperial vehicles are used for scouting and patrolling, while high-ranking officers travel in style aboard Star Destroyers and luxury Imperial Shuttles.

ALL TERRAIN SCOUT TRANSPORT (AT-ST)

ALL TERRAIN ARMOURED TRANSPORT (AT-AT)

COMMANDERS HAVE GOOD VIEW OF BATTLEFIELD

HEAVY ARMOUR WITHSTANDS BLASTER FIRE

LEGS GIVE EXCELLENT MOVEMENT OVER UNEVEN SURFACES

HUGE FEET CRUSH ENEMIES

LAND

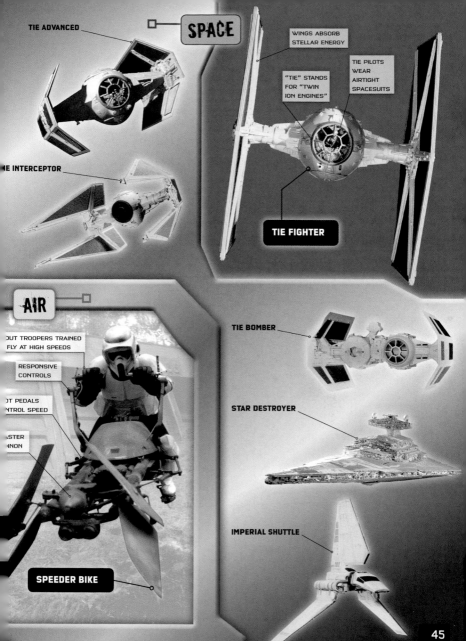

TIE ADVANCED

SPACE

WINGS ABSORB STELLAR ENERGY

TIE PILOTS WEAR AIRTIGHT SPACESUITS

"TIE" STANDS FOR "TWIN ION ENGINES"

E INTERCEPTOR

TIE FIGHTER

AIR

TIE BOMBER

OUT TROOPERS TRAINED FLY AT HIGH SPEEDS

RESPONSIVE CONTROLS

STAR DESTROYER

OT PEDALS NTROL SPEED

STER NNON

IMPERIAL SHUTTLE

SPEEDER BIKE

45

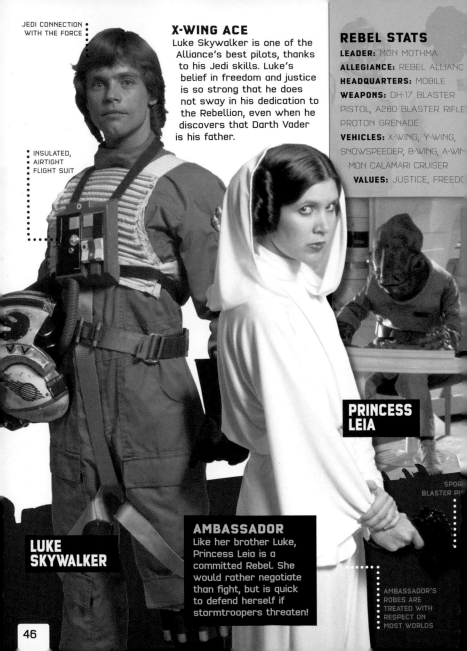

X-WING ACE

Luke Skywalker is one of the Alliance's best pilots, thanks to his Jedi skills. Luke's belief in freedom and justice is so strong that he does not sway in his dedication to the Rebellion, even when he discovers that Darth Vader is his father.

INSULATED,
AIRTIGHT
FLIGHT SUIT

REBEL STATS

LEADER: MON MOTHMA
ALLEGIANCE: REBEL ALLIANC
HEADQUARTERS: MOBILE
WEAPONS: DH-17 BLASTER
PISTOL, A280 BLASTER RIFLE
PROTON GRENADE
VEHICLES: X-WING, Y-WING,
SNOWSPEEDER, B-WING, A-WIN
MON CALAMARI CRUISER
VALUES: JUSTICE, FREEDC

PRINCESS LEIA

LUKE SKYWALKER

AMBASSADOR

Like her brother Luke, Princess Leia is a committed Rebel. She would rather negotiate than fight, but is quick to defend herself if stormtroopers threaten!

SPOR
BLASTER PI

AMBASSADOR'S
ROBES ARE
TREATED WITH
RESPECT ON
MOST WORLDS

CHAIN OF COMMAND

MON MOTHMA

REBEL GENERALS/ADMIRALS

REBEL OFFICERS

REBEL TROOPERS

ALLIANCE LEADERS

Mon Mothma, the senator from Chandrila, commands all the Rebel forces. Before each mission she meets with her Generals and Admirals to get their advice.

ADMIRAL ACKBAR

The navy is the backbone of the Rebel military. Admiral Ackbar and his people, the Mon Calamari, supply huge warships that can stand up to Imperial Star Destroyers. Ackbar is a brilliant commander who doesn't like to take foolish risks.

Rebel
ALLIANCE

The brave soldiers of the Rebel Alliance join together to defeat the Empire or die trying! Based in secret hideouts and using patched-together equipment, these hopeful volunteers must stay one step ahead of Darth Vader and the mighty Imperial military.

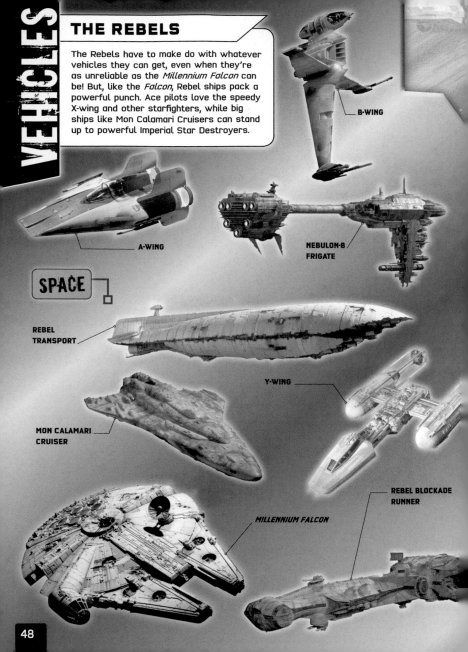

THE REBELS

The Rebels have to make do with whatever vehicles they can get, even when they're as unreliable as the *Millennium Falcon* can be! But, like the *Falcon*, Rebel ships pack a powerful punch. Ace pilots love the speedy X-wing and other starfighters, while big ships like Mon Calamari Cruisers can stand up to powerful Imperial Star Destroyers.

B-WING

A-WING

NEBULON-B FRIGATE

SPACE

REBEL TRANSPORT

Y-WING

MON CALAMARI CRUISER

REBEL BLOCKADE RUNNER

MILLENNIUM FALCON

48

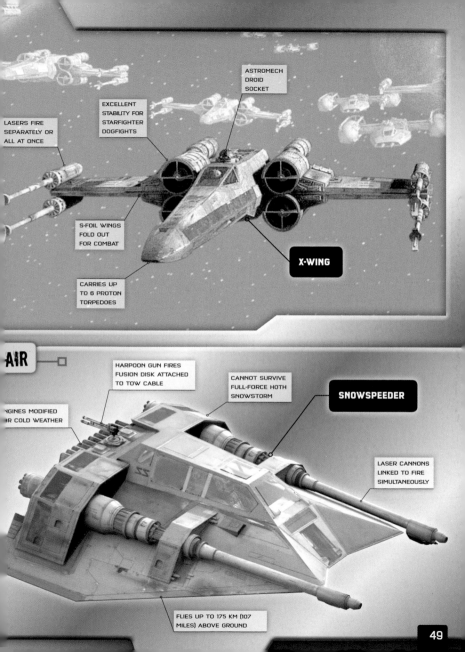

LASERS FIRE
SEPARATELY OR
ALL AT ONCE

EXCELLENT
STABILITY FOR
STARFIGHTER
DOGFIGHTS

ASTROMECH
DROID
SOCKET

S-FOIL WINGS
FOLD OUT
FOR COMBAT

X-WING

CARRIES UP
TO 6 PROTON
TORPEDOES

AIR

HARPOON GUN FIRES
FUSION DISK ATTACHED
TO TOW CABLE

CANNOT SURVIVE
FULL-FORCE HOTH
SNOWSTORM

SNOWSPEEDER

NGINES MODIFIED
R COLD WEATHER

LASER CANNONS
LINKED TO FIRE
SIMULTANEOUSLY

FLIES UP TO 175 KM (107
MILES) ABOVE GROUND

VILLAGE CHIEFTAIN
(CHIEF CHIRPA)

COUNCIL OF ELDERS

WAR CHIEFS

EWOK WARRIORS

UNLIKELY FRIENDS

Visitors to Endor's moon are rare, and
Ewoks are suspicious of outsiders. At
first, they try to cook Han and Luke for
dinner, but the Ewoks soon realise that
the Rebels can help them keep their
village safe from worse strangers.

In the dense forest of Endor, the
Ewoks have a military advantage over
the invading stormtroopers. They know
every part of the terrain like the back
of their paws, and they blend in with
the forest colours.

Ewok WARRIORS

Ewoks may be small and furry, but watch out – these prou
creatures can be fierce. The Ewoks don't know anything
about the Galactic Civil War, but they do know that Imperi
stormtroopers aren't welcome on their forest moon!

50

EWOK STATS

LEADER: CHIEF CHIRPA
ALLEGIANCE: REBEL ALLIANCE
HEADQUARTERS: BRIGHT TREE VILLAGE, MOON OF ENDOR
WEAPONS: CATAPULTS, LOG TRAPS, SNARES, ARROWS, SPEARS, BOLAS
VEHICLES: HANG GLIDERS, WAR WAGONS
VALUES: TRIBAL LOYALTY, PRESERVING NATURE

FIREPOWER
Ewok weapons and equipment made of wood, rope and animal skins may look primitive, but with teamwork, the Ewoks are smart enough to defeat stormtroopers.

WISE LEADER
Chief Chirpa is the leader of the Ewoks who are drawn into war when their moon is chosen as the site for the Death Star's shield generator. Chirpa might not lead a trained army, but his tribe are brave, fierce and determined to protect their home from the Empire.

HOODS ARE A SIGN OF ADULTHOOD

CHIEF CHIRPA

CHIRPA BELIEVES THAT HIS MEDALLION HAS MYSTICAL POWERS

CEREMONIAL KNIFE IS A SYMBOL OF HIGH RANK

WICKET W. WARRICK

WICKET'S FAVOURITE WEAPONS ARE THE SPEAR AND THE BOLA

INQUISITIVE SCOUT
Wicket is a scout who gets more than he expects when he finds Princess Leia in the forest. His curiosity is matched by his bravery in the Battle of Endor.

51

PEACE INTERRUPTED

AFTER YEARS OF REBELLION, the death of Emperor Palpatine gave the oppressed peoples of the galaxy undeniable evidence that the Empire could be defeated. A longing for freedom and peace drove a great tide of revolution from sector to sector, to the point where a truce – unthinkable at the height of the Galactic Civil War – was signed between the New Republic and the weakened Empire. As one of its first acts, the restored Senate promptly passed the Military Disarmament Act. Many were convinced that the age of galaxy-wide conflict was over.

THE NEW REPUBLIC

Following its great victory against the Empire at the Battle of Endor, the Alliance to Restore the Republic rebranded itself as the New Republic, and shortly afterward a peace treaty – the Galactic Concordance – was signed with the remnants of the Empire. Believing that the Empire was no longer a threat, the New Republic turned its attention to reshaping galactic politics.

THE FIRST ORDER

The Galactic Concordance defanged the Empire's ability to wage war, with strict disarmament treaties and punishing reparations. The Old Empire withered away, becoming a remnant of political hardliners locked in a cold war with the New Republic, before eventually breaking away to reform in the Unknown Regions as the mysterious First Order.

THE RESISTANCE

The Resistance is a small private force created by Princess Leia Organa to keep watch on the movements of the First Order. Though she petitions the New Republic government for support, she finds the politics of the Senate too slow and too mired in self-interest to be of any help. The New Republic tolerates the Resistance, though it is wary of risking war with the First Order.

Dantooine

Moraband

Yavin

Felucia

Dathomir

Ithor

Mandalore

'ler Base Origin Point

Ord Mantell

INNER RIM

Onderon

Kashyyyk

Coruscant

Kuat

UNKNOWN REGIONS

Rakata Prime

CORE

Corellia

Nal Hutta

EXPANSION REGION

Jakku

Hosnian Prime

COLONIES

Bothawui

Takodana

MID RIM

Rattatak

Malastare

Tatooine

Endor

Geonosis

Naboo

WESTERN REACHES

Sullust

Bespin and Hoth

D'Qar

Dagobah

Utapau

OUTER RIM

POE DAMERON

POE DAMERON GREW UP hearing the legends of the starfighter jockeys of old, having been raised by veterans of the Rebel Alliance. At 32 years old, Poe is now the most daring and skilled of the Resistance pilots. His appetite for risk is indulged by even the most serious minded Resistance commanders, as he gets spectacular results when pitted against First Order starfighter patrols. Though brash, Poe has great charisma and limitless respect for the idealistic founders of the Resistance, particularly his idol, General Leia Organa.

REBEL ROOTS

Poe Dameron was born toward the explosive finale of the war between the Rebel Alliance and the Galactic Empire. His mother, Shara, was an Alliance fighter pilot while his father, Kes, also served in the rebel military. Poe was raised on Yavin 4, in a newly established colony not far from the Massassi ruins from which the Rebel Alliance launched the fateful mission that destroyed the first Death Star.

CUSTOMISED X-WING

Poe's *Black One* is a customised Incom-FreiTek T-70 X-wing fighter co[c] with sensor-scattering ferrosphere pa[ ] Though often overlooked by sensors, colours certainly stand out to the org[ ] eye. BB-8 considers *Black One* the be[ ] and smoothest ride of Poe's ships.

Macroscope adjustment controls

Stock with gas reservoir

Sealed blaster lasing chamber

Remova[ ] galven-[ ] barrel ti[ ]

POE'S BLASTER RIFLE

Trigger guard

Resistance commander ground uniform

Reckless Poe has been in many tight spots throughout his adventures, but even he is helpless before the overwhelming power commanded by Kylo Ren, enforcer of the First Order.

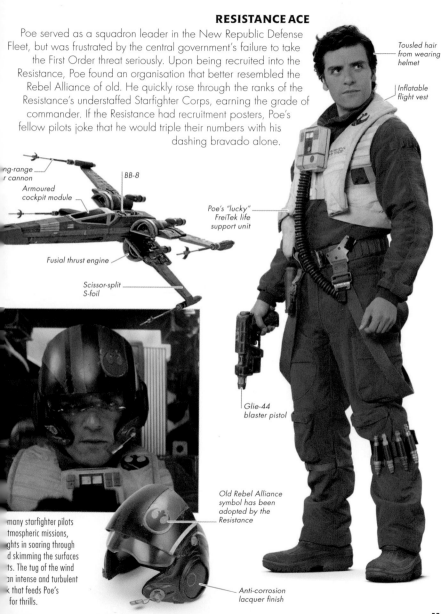

RESISTANCE ACE

Poe served as a squadron leader in the New Republic Defense Fleet, but was frustrated by the central government's failure to take the First Order threat seriously. Upon being recruited into the Resistance, Poe found an organisation that better resembled the Rebel Alliance of old. He quickly rose through the ranks of the Resistance's understaffed Starfighter Corps, earning the grade of commander. If the Resistance had recruitment posters, Poe's fellow pilots joke that he would triple their numbers with his dashing bravado alone.

Tousled hair from wearing helmet

Inflatable flight vest

ng-range r cannon

BB-8

Armoured cockpit module

Poe's "lucky" FreiTek life support unit

Fusial thrust engine

Scissor-split S-foil

Glie-44 blaster pistol

many starfighter pilots tmospheric missions, ghts in soaring through d skimming the surfaces ts. The tug of the wind an intense and turbulent k that feeds Poe's for thrills.

Old Rebel Alliance symbol has been adopted by the Resistance

Anti-corrosion lacquer finish

FINN

AFTER THE RAID on Jakku, questions arise regarding FN-2187's competence on the battlefield. He is scheduled to undergo "renewal therapy" to ensure his unquestioning loyalty to the First Order, but before that happens, FN-2187 has a profound change of heart, and becomes a fugitive. He adopts the name "Finn" instead of his numerical designation, the only identity he has ever known. It would seem that Finn's good nature could not be wiped from his mind as it is from others who undergo stormtrooper training.

Resistance fighter jacket, "borrowed" from Poe Dameron

DESERTER

Once the rush of escape fades and Finn has a moment to collect his thoughts, he begins to realise the enormity of his actions. Having made an enemy of Kylo Ren means Finn must keep running. Knowing very little of the galaxy's workings beyond the borders of the First Order, Finn at first considers joining a pirate crew. But such thoughts instantly vaporise when the First Order strikes again, and reveals the unrivalled power of its ultimate weapon — a weapon that Finn served in the shadow of.

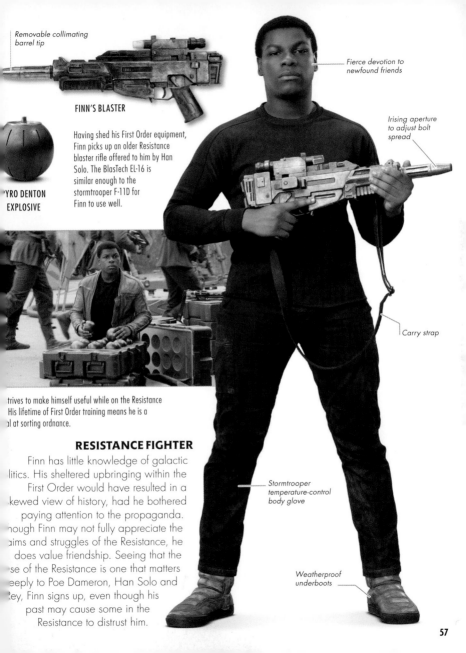

Removable collimating
barrel tip

FINN'S BLASTER

Having shed his First Order equipment,
Finn picks up an older Resistance
blaster rifle offered to him by Han
Solo. The BlasTech EL-16 is
similar enough to the
stormtrooper F-11D for
Finn to use well.

YRO DENTON
EXPLOSIVE

Fierce devotion to
newfound friends

Irising aperture
to adjust bolt
spread

Carry strap

trives to make himself useful while on the Resistance
His lifetime of First Order training means he is a
al at sorting ordnance.

RESISTANCE FIGHTER

Finn has little knowledge of galactic
litics. His sheltered upbringing within the
First Order would have resulted in a
kewed view of history, had he bothered
paying attention to the propaganda.
hough Finn may not fully appreciate the
aims and struggles of the Resistance, he
does value friendship. Seeing that the
se of the Resistance is one that matters
eeply to Poe Dameron, Han Solo and
ey, Finn signs up, even though his
past may cause some in the
Resistance to distrust him.

Stormtrooper
temperature-control
body glove

Weatherproof
underboots

KYLO REN

STRIDING ONTO RAVAGED BATTLEFIELDS with bold purpose, his singed robes whirling about his lean frame, is the mysterious Kylo Ren. His body radiates with suppressed anger, a fiery temper kept in check and honed to a deadly point. Though Ren often arrives after his stormtroopers have secured victory, he has no fear of battle. His ability to use the Force grants him many impressive combat skills, but Kylo Ren is no Jedi, nor is he a Sith. He is the archetype of a new generation of dark side users that have emerged to fill the void left by the Sith's demise.

INTERROGATION

To ensure the First Order remains unchallenged, Kylo Ren has been tasked with hunting down any remnants of the Jedi. The dark warrior employs torture on his helpless captives, using a disturbing array of pain-inflicting devices. Beyond such tools, Kylo is skilled at using the Force to probe the minds of the unwilling, tearing loose deeply held secrets.

INTERROGATION CHAIR

Similar to devices developed by the Inquisitorius of the Galactic Empire, Kylo Ren's interrogation chair is a collection of pain-causing implements distributed along a prisoner-confining frame.

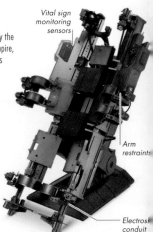

Vital sign monitoring sensors

Arm restraints

INTERROGATION TOOLS

Electros... conduit

Silver inlay radiates from the eyes as a symbol of power

Hinged mechanism seals tightly when shut

Integrated vocabulator projects Ren's voice

VADER'S MASK

Scavenged from a funeral pyre on Endor, Darth Vader's charred and melted helmet is a silent symbol of both the dark side's power and its weakness.

KYLO REN'S HELMET

Patterned after the battle gear of the Knights of Ren, Kylo Ren's helmet conceals his identity and adds to his imposing demeanour. Servomotors drive articulated arms that separate the face mask from the helmet, letting Kylo remove the black form to stare down his opponents with uncontained malice.

vl is a remnant
om Ren's early
training

Turbolaser
battery

Tractor
beam
projectors

Central
flight deck

THE *FINALIZER*

Constructed in a secret shipyard within the Unknown Regions, the *Finalizer* is a clear violation of New Republic disarmament treaties.

COMMAND SHIPS

Kylo Ren commands from the bridge of the *Finalizer*, a *Resurgent*-class Star Destroyer bristling with firepower. At nearly 3,000 metres long, it is almost twice the size of the Old Empire's Star Destroyers. For travel to planetary surfaces, Kylo uses an *Upsilon*-class shuttle, with towering wings that cut an imposing profile. The crews of both ships know to be wary of Ren's volatile temper.

Unstable
serrated
plasma
blade

After the subjugation of Tuanul village on Jakku, Kylo Ren emerges onto the smouldering battlefield to personally interrogate any high-value prisoners.

FIRST ORDER WARRIOR

Kylo Ren exists outside the formal command structure of the First Order, and has a direct link to the shadowy Supreme Leader who is ultimately in charge of these forces of darkness. It is with palpable tension that the upper command of the First Order contends with Kylo, as his agenda always trumps military objectives. In this way, Kylo's placement within the hierarchy resembles that of Darth Vader in the old Galactic Empire. This is entirely by design.

REY

Skin has
adapted
extreme
radiatio

LIFE ON JAKKU is tough – it is a daily struggle for survival on the harsh planet. Nineteen-year-old Rey has carved out her existence on this bleak frontier world. Each day she has marked her victory over the searing sunlight, scorching sands and cutthroat scavengers with a scratch along the wall of her makeshift home. Thousands of scratches are a testament to her tenacity and survivor's instinct. Despite a life that should have built a barrier against any sympathy or weakness, Rey still possesses a generous heart and a willingness to help those in need.

Tight bin
keep out t
sun and s

REY'S HOUSE

Rey lives in a toppled AT-AT walker, not far from the junkfields that surround Niima Outpost. A hatch in the walker's exposed belly leads to the sloping interior that Rey calls home. Here, she refurbishes scrap prior to trading it, and sleeps in a simple hammock.

Satchel holds tools
and small salvage

LIVING ALONE

Rey is a gifted mechanic, seemingly having an innate sense of how machinery fits together and functions. Having grown up in the shadows of last-generation war technology, she is comfortable around vehicles and weapons. She has also become a skilled pilot, despite showing no desire ever to leave her desolate world. Her only escapes from the brutal conditions of Jakku are vivid flights of imagination, where she envisions lush, green worlds and fantasises about a family she has never known.

Primary heat exchanger

Netting filled with salvage

Windscreen

The forward intake grill directs air into a dual turbojet assembly, producing turbocharged thrust for incredible speeds.

Afterburner assembly

Salvaged quarterstaff

'S SPEEDER

junker speeder is a cobbled-together transport that uilt for travel across the Jakku wilderness. The craft etween the classifications of speeder bike and p, not quite fitting in either category. A modified r web keeps Rey in place as the speeder rockets immense speeds, and well-positioned heat sinks the engine thrusters from burning her.

Survival equipment stored inside

hicle favours speed over cargo capacity, meaning she en make return trips to carry salvage into town. Rey that smaller hauls are easier to defend; a greedy er quickly draws rivals.

Govath-wool traveller's boots

SCAVENGER

Rey's daily routine on Jakku consists of treks into the junkfields, where she explores inside the massive wrecks, scavenging valuable pieces of technology. She brings her haul to Niima Outpost, where she trades it for food. Climbing through decaying Star Destroyers or Star Cruisers requires Rey to be in peak physical shape, and she must also be ready to defend herself against cutthroat thieves who roam the wastes.

STORMTROOPERS

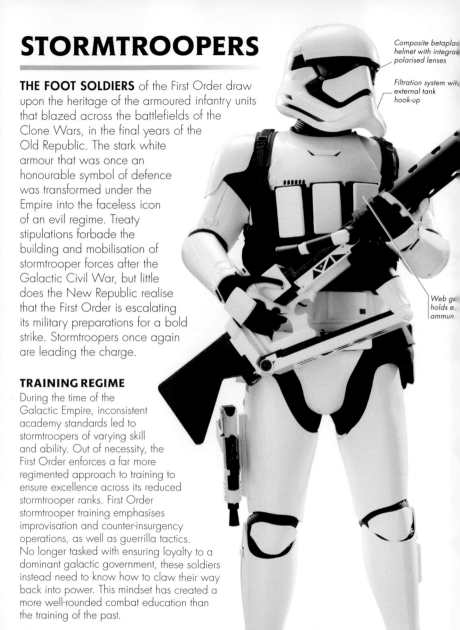

THE FOOT SOLDIERS of the First Order draw upon the heritage of the armoured infantry units that blazed across the battlefields of the Clone Wars, in the final years of the Old Republic. The stark white armour that was once an honourable symbol of defence was transformed under the Empire into the faceless icon of an evil regime. Treaty stipulations forbade the building and mobilisation of stormtrooper forces after the Galactic Civil War, but little does the New Republic realise that the First Order is escalating its military preparations for a bold strike. Stormtroopers once again are leading the charge.

TRAINING REGIME

During the time of the Galactic Empire, inconsistent academy standards led to stormtroopers of varying skill and ability. Out of necessity, the First Order enforces a far more regimented approach to training to ensure excellence across its reduced stormtrooper ranks. First Order stormtrooper training emphasises improvisation and counter-insurgency operations, as well as guerrilla tactics. No longer tasked with ensuring loyalty to a dominant galactic government, these soldiers instead need to know how to claw their way back into power. This mindset has created a more well-rounded combat education than the training of the past.

Composite betaplas helmet with integra polarised lenses

Filtration system wit external tank hook-up

Web ge holds e ammun

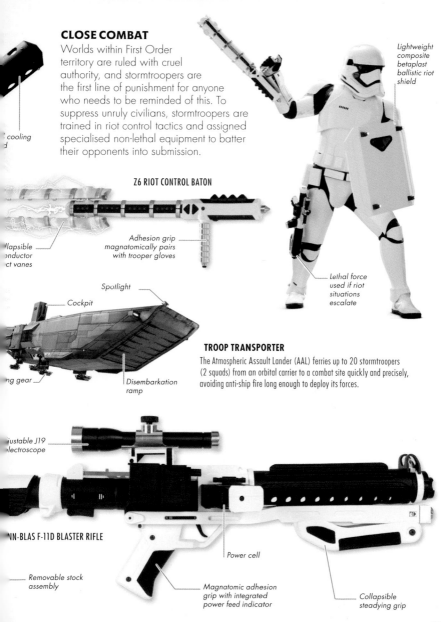

CLOSE COMBAT

Worlds within First Order territory are ruled with cruel authority, and stormtroopers are the first line of punishment for anyone who needs to be reminded of this. To suppress unruly civilians, stormtroopers are trained in riot control tactics and assigned specialised non-lethal equipment to batter their opponents into submission.

Lightweight composite betaplast ballistic riot shield

' cooling
d

Z6 RIOT CONTROL BATON

llapsible
onductor
ct vanes

Adhesion grip
magnatomically pairs
with trooper gloves

Lethal force used if riot situations escalate

Spotlight

Cockpit

ng gear

Disembarkation ramp

TROOP TRANSPORTER

The Atmospheric Assault Lander (AAL) ferries up to 20 stormtroopers (2 squads) from an orbital carrier to a combat site quickly and precisely, avoiding anti-ship fire long enough to deploy its forces.

justable J19
lectroscope

NN-BLAS F-11D BLASTER RIFLE

Removable stock
assembly

Power cell

Magnatomic adhesion grip with integrated power feed indicator

Collapsible steadying grip

BB-8

AN INTENSELY LOYAL astromech, BB-8 bravely rolls into danger when carrying out its assignments. The droid becomes the subject of an intense First Order search when it carries information that could lead to Luke Skywalker.

DATA FILE

AFFILIATION: Resistance
TYPE: Astromech droid
MANUFACTURER: Unknown
HEIGHT: 0.67m (2ft 2in)
APPEARANCES: VII

High frequency receiver antenna

BALL DROID

A complex drive system and wireless telemetry keep BB-8 on the move, tumbling its body forwards while keeping its head upright. When situations require greater stability, BB-8 can deploy cables from compressed launchers that then anchor the droid in place, or allow it to reel itself into hard-to-reach places.

Primary photoreceptor

As an astromech droid, BB-8's small, spherical body is designed to fit into the droid socket of an X-wing starfighter. From that position BB-8 can manage the essential systems of the vessel, make repairs and plot courses through space.

BB-8 speaks in beeps and whirs, and can project holograms.

Swappable tool bay

CHEWBACCA

CHEWBACCA is a Wookiee mechanic and pilot. During the Clone Wars, he fights to defend his planet. In the time of the Empire, he is first mate and loyal friend to Han Solo aboard the *Millennium Falcon*.

Thirty years after the Rebellion, Han and Chewie are still side by side.

WOOKIEE MECHANIC

The great Wookiee uses his mechanical abilities to keep Solo's starship flying. Later, he will employ these skills to completely reconstruct C-3PO after the poor droid is blasted apart on Cloud City.

Tool pouch

Bowcaster

Water-shedding hair

DATA FILE

AFFILIATION: Rebel Alliance/ Resistance
HOMEWORLD: Kashyyyk
SPECIES: Wookiee
HEIGHT: 2.28m (7ft 6in)
APPEARANCES: Clone Wars, III, IV, V, VI, VII

Chewie serves as Han Solo's fiercely loyal co-pilot and trusty fellow adventurer. He enjoys the thrilling action that Solo gets them into, but sometimes tries to act as a check on his partner's recklessness.

TAKE THE

STAR WARS

GALAXY HOME TODAY